Tammy & Jinty Remixed

TREASURY OF BRITISH COMICS

Rebellion

WELCOME TO TAMMY & JINTY REMIXED!

You may not know this, but **Tammy** and **Jinty** were two comics which were published in the 1970s and 1980s — back when your mothers and grandmothers were young. At that time, comics were divided into 'girls' comics and 'boys' comics, and **Tammy & Jinty** covered almost every facet of girls' lives — school, sports, friendship, rivalry, romance, the apocalypse, ghosts, witchcraft, parallel universes, aliens and everything in between! When we asked writers and artists to give us 'new' **Tammy & Jinty** stories, some of them took the old comics and characters as their starting point and reimagined them, whereas others created brand new worlds. The result? **Tammy & Jinty Remixed**! This book is bursting at the seams with comics about adventure, friendship, magic and superpowers, as well as a couple of vintage **Tammy & Jinty** comics. This comic is for everyone and anyone, but most importantly, this book is for you. We hope you enjoy it.

The Tammy & Jinty Team.

Contents

ROCKY OF THE ROVERS
BY ROB WILLIAMS & LISA HENKE
PAGES 4 - 8

SPEED DEMONS
BY SARAH MILLMAN
PAGES 9 - 13

BELLA AT THE BAR
BY RACHAEL BALL & VANESSA CARDINALI
PAGES 18 - 23

DUCKFACE
BY RACHAEL SMITH & YISHAN LI
PAGES 25 - 29

BOARDING SCHOOL
BY RACHAEL SMITH & YISHAN LI
PAGES 30 - 51

THE EGNIMA VARIATION
BY GRAINNE McENTEE & DANI
PAGES 60 - 64

IN THE COLD DARK
BY MATT GIBBS & V.V. GLASS
PAGES 65 - 69

MAISIE'S MAGIC EYE
BY KATE ASHWIN & KEL McDONALD
PAGES 70 - 73

AFFIRMATIVE ACTION
BY ANDY W. CLIFT
PAGES 74 - 77

JUSTINE THE JUSTICE
BY EMMA BEEBY & P.J. HOLDEN
PAGES 78 - 83

CAT GIRL RETURNS
BY RAMZEE & ELKYS NOVA
PAGES 92 - 105

RETRO STRIPS
BELLA AT THE BAR PAGES 15 - 17
SALLY WAS A CAT PAGES 52 - 58
THE CAT GIRL PAGES 85 - 90

MEET THE CREATORS
RACHAEL SMITH PAGE 24
DANI PAGE 59
RAMZEE PAGE 91

BEHIND THE SCENES
PAGES 106 - 107

ROCKY OF THE ROVERS

THIS IS ROY.

ROY RACE.

'ROY OF THE ROVERS', APPARENTLY...STAR STRIKER.

HE'S AN IDIOT.

GET *OFF* ME, ROCKY!

IT'S *TUESDAY!* SO IT'S *MY* TURN IN THE FRONT SEAT.

IT'S *WEDNESDAY!*

SEE WHAT I MEAN?

GULP!

MUM! ROCKY PUNCHED ME!

HOW DO YOU COPE WITH THOSE BIG CENTRE HALVES WHEN I GIVE YOU A TINY LITTLE ELBOW IN THE RIBS AND YOU MAKE THIS MUCH FUSS?

SHE'S A LUNATIC, MUM! SHE'S GETTING WORSE!

WHILE HE'S OFF THINKING HE'S A BIG SHOT WITH MELCHESTER ROVERS, I PLAY FOR THE LOCAL WOMEN'S TEAM--*SOWERBY.*

EVERYONE IN MELCHESTER BANGS ON AND ON (AND ON) ABOUT ROY AND HIS ROCKET SHOT, BUT HERE'S WHAT THEY DON'T KNOW...

YET.

I'M GOING TO BE THE BEST FOOTBALLER IN THE COUNTRY.

THUNK

GOOD TACKLE, ROCKY!

SCRIPT ROB WILLIAMS • **ART** LISA HENKE • **COLOURS** JOHN CHARLES • **LETTERS** JIM CAMPBELL

FFION GUTHRIE. CAPTAIN AND PLAYER COACH FOR SOWERBY. BEEN PICKED TO PLAY FOR THE WALES U-17s WOMEN'S TEAM.

I DON'T CARE WHAT SHE THINKS OF ME.

YOU'RE REALLY COMING ALONG. BUT STAY ON YOUR FEET JUST IN CASE YOU MISTIME ONE OF THOSE, OK?

YAY! (I THINK).

KCLAP

BIG GAME ON SATURDAY VS BURNDEAN, GIRLS. THEY'RE USEFUL. WELL ORGANISED. GOT TWO ENGLAND U-17 INTER-NATIONALS.

I THINK THE NATIONAL SCOUTS ARE COMING ALONG FOR THAT REASON. IF YOU NEED ENCOURAGEMENT!

TEAM WILL BE UP ON THE NOTICEBOARD TONIGHT.

UH... FFION.

YEAH, ROCKY.

TIP

I WANT TO PLAY STRIKER. I MEAN...I...I THINK THAT'S MY BEST POSITION.

I KNOW YOU DO, ROCKY.

TEAM SHEET'LL BE UP LATER, LIKE I SAID.

YES!

RIGHT, COME ON...IF ROY CAN DO IT, YOU DEFINITELY...

YOU? UP FRONT? DON'T MAKE ME LAUGH.

TAP

DON'T MAKE US LAUGH.

UGH. THE MILLERS. THE WORST.

YEAH, RIGHT, SIS. DON'T GET CARRIED AWAY, RACE. YOU'RE NOT EXACTLY YOUR BROTHER.

SOWERBY vs BURNDEAN.
LEAGUE MATCH.

NO, YOU'RE NOT.

YOU'RE TOUGH AND RELENTLESS. YOU'RE SCRAPPY. YOU'VE GOT ENERGY TO BURN, TONNES OF PASSION AND YOU'RE A *REALLY* GOOD TACKLER.

YOU'RE YOUR OWN PERSON. SO: EMBRACE ALL THAT.

USE THAT!

SO. TURNS OUT I'M NOT MY BROTHER...

AND, TRUTH BE TOLD, HE'S NOT AN IDIOT.... DON'T TELL HIM I SAID THAT, MIND YOU!

WELL IN, ROCKY!

THUNK

I'M DIFFERENT.

THAT'S A GOOD BALL!

I'M MY OWN PERSON.

PHWEEET

GOAL! SOWERBY. 1-1!

"I'M ROCKY RACE. ROCKY OF SOWERBY."

GET IN, GIRLS! COME ON! LET'S HAVE ANOTHER!

"AND I'M GOING TO BE THE BEST *DEFENSIVE MIDFIELDER* IN THE COUNTRY."

THE END

SPEED DEMONS

SCRIPT & ART SARAH MILLMAN
LETTERS JIM CAMPBELL

ALRIGHT, SPEED DEMONS! GATHER ROUND!

TIME TO ANNOUNCE WHO'LL BE JOINING ME-- LUCY THE LASER--IN OUR MATCH TOMORROW...

OUR FIRST MATCH IN THE SOUTH EAST ROLLER DERBY LEAGUE 2019!

I WANT YOU ALL TO PLEASE PUT YOUR HANDS TOGETHER FOR...MARY MURDER!

ANTHRAX AMY!

POLLY POCKET ROCKET!

AAAAND-- MEL-O-DIE!

DON'T BE DISAPPOINTED, DAISY--YOU'RE STILL NEW. LUCY JUST WANTS TO EASE YOU IN.

I'M NOT-- REALLY! IF ANYTHING, I'M RELIEVED.

I BET IT'S BECAUSE YOU DON'T HAVE YOUR KILLER NICKNAME READY YET!

"POLLY POCKET"? REALLY?

WHAT? I LOVED THOSE AS A KID! AS IF "ANTHRAX AMY" WAS ANY BETTER...

SO... MEL-O-DIE-- YOU'RE THE JAMMER TOMORROW. YOU NERVOUS?

NO.

Ooh, SOMEBODY'S CONFIDENT!

HEY, MEL!

WELL, LET'S JUST SAY...I'VE GOT A TRICK UP MY SLEEVE.

THE END

behind the scenes
Bella at the Bar

Bella at the bar (also known as "That Barlow Kid", or just "Bella"), first ran in **Tammy**, 22nd June 1974. It was drawn by John Amstrong from 1974 to 1984. Writers included Jenny McDade, John Wagner, Primrose Cumming and Malcolm Shaw.

It was one of the one most popular strips in British girls' comics. Created by Jenny McDade and John Armstrong, Bella is a hardworking, talented working class girl, who lives with her mean, crooked Aunt and Uncle and dreams of being a gymnast. Many hardships are thrown her way, but with hard work, determination and athleticism, Bella is able to overcome all manner of adversity!

Girls' comics in the UK would often focus on the difficulties and discrimination poorer girls faced everyday, whether in school, work or at play. Bella's ongoing fight against poverty meant she was an icon to many working class girls when she was first published.

The reimagining of *Bella at the Bar*, by Rachael Ball and Vanessa Cardinali, places Bella in the modern day but keeps the tension between the working class Bella and the wealthy world of gymnastics. Like the original *Bella* which ran in the 1970s and 1980s, this comic tells us to never give up, never judge a book (or person) by its cover, and to follow your dreams!

IT STARTS TODAY: Meet the youngest window cleaner around — one with an even higher ambition

Bella at the Bar

Bella Barlow lived in the seedy terraced home of her uncle Jed and aunt Gertrude. Inside the home Bella did all the cooking and cleaning. Outside her days were spent helping Jed in his window cleaning. But every spare moment she had was spent out in the tiny back garden, with an old bar she had made. . .

OI — BELLA! QUIT MONKEYIN' ABOUT ON THAT OLD BIT OF WOOD! YOUR UNCLE JED'S WAITIN' FOR YOU!

WATCH IT, AUNT GERT — NEARLY MADE ME LOSE MY BALANCE.

HURRY IT UP, GIRL! WE GOT NEARLY THE WHOLE OF DOWNSIDE CRESCENT'S WINDOWS TO DO.

THEY'RE BIG BUILDINGS — THAT MEANS THE LONGEST LADDER.

UP YOU GO AND MIND YOU CLEAN ALL THE WINDOW CORNERS — I DON'T WANT ANY COMPLAINTS.

YES, UNCLE JED.

WHEW — PEACE AND QUIET FROM UNCLE JED AT LAST UP HERE. LUCKY I LIKE HEIGHTS.

GOLLY — IT'S A GYM IN THERE! AND SOMEBODY'S DOING SOME TRICKS ON A BAR — A PROPER BAR!

WOW — SHE'S SUPERB ON IT! WISH I COULD TRY THAT. MUST BE DIFFICULT KEEPIN' YOUR BALANCE AND LOOKIN' LOVELY. . .

BELLA! YOU GONE TO SLEEP UP THERE! GET ON WITH IT OR I'LL TAN THE HIDE OFF YOU!

DON'T WORRY — I'VE DONE MY WINDOWS, UNCLE JED. I'M COMING DOWN!

FOR PETE'S SAKE, GIRL — MIND THAT BUCKET OF YOURS!

SCRIPT JENNY McDADE • **ART** JOHN ARMSTRONG

I'LL NEVER BE AS GOOD AS YOU! YOU'RE AMAZING!

THANKS, BUT YOU NEED MORE THAN TALENT TO MAKE IT.

MY SCHOOL'S NOTHING LIKE THIS.

GYMNASTICS IS MORE MY MUM'S DREAM THAN MINE.

STREET DANCE IS MY THING.

REALLY? SHOW ME!

OK--BUT NO LAUGHING...

WOW, THAT'S GREAT! YOU'RE REALLY TALENTED, NINA!

YEAH, NO ONE CARES ABOUT STREET DANCE ROUND HERE THOUGH.

YOU SHOULD TELL YOUR MUM THAT GYMNASTICS ISN'T FOR YOU. SHE'D UNDERSTAND.

I CAN'T! MY SISTER TINA DIED LAST YEAR. SHE WAS A BRILLIANT GYMNAST. IF I GIVE UP, IT WOULD BREAK MY MUM'S HEART.

OH, I'M SORRY, LOVE.

I'VE JUST GOT TO TURN THE LIGHTS OUT. COME WITH ME?

SURE.

IT'S OK, YOU CAN LEAVE MY BAG THERE.

YOU GONNA ENTER THE TRIALS?

YOU'RE JOKING! I'D MAKE A RIGHT FOOL OF MYSELF! *YOU* SHOULD THOUGH!

YEAH, RIGHT! I'M NOT AN ELITE GIRL!

YOU CAN ENTER UNDER MY NAME!

IS THAT EVEN LEGAL?!

IT IS NOW!

Nina Harries

NINA! NO!

HAHAHA! YOU'VE GOT TO DO IT NOW!

OH, NO! TINA'S LOCKET! IT'S GONE!

BUT I...

HAVE YOU LOOKED IN ALL THE POCKETS?!

YES! ⌇SNIFF⌇ IT'S ALL I HAVE LEFT OF HER...

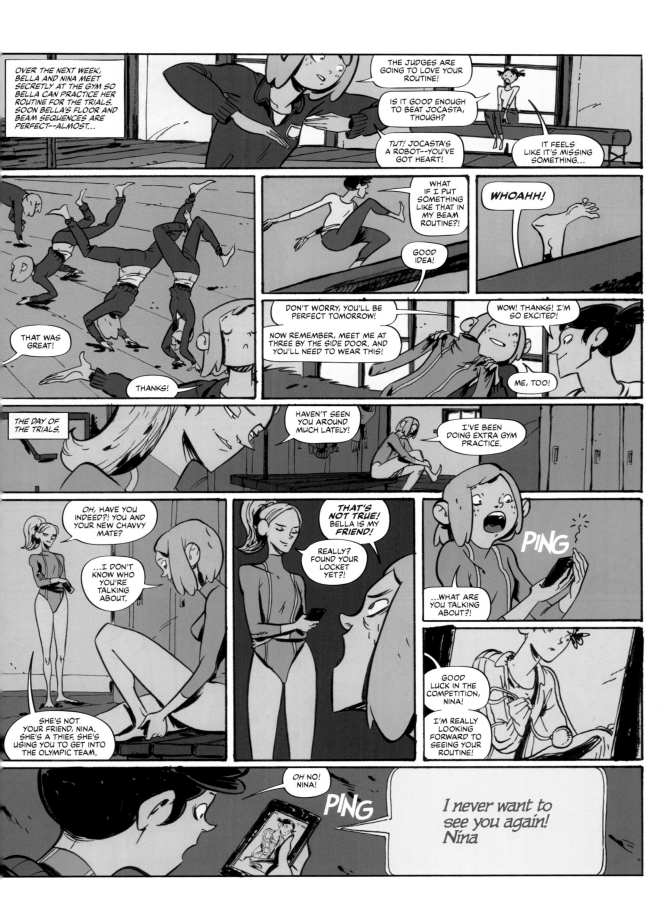

meet the creator
RACHAEL SMITH

FRAN OF THE FLOODS, ART BY PHIL GASCOINE

Q1. How did you start making comics?
I've always drawn, ever since I was old enough to hold a pencil. I didn't come to storytelling until I was a bit older – maybe in my early teens. In my early 20s I figured out that comics were the perfect marriage of drawing and storytelling and I've never looked back!

Q2. What's your advice for making a comic?
Start now, but start small. Take life drawing lessons, if you can. Read as many books as possible. Not just comics, read novels and news stories and magazines, engage with stories in all their wonderful forms.

Q3. You have two stories in this book, *Duckface* and *Boarding School*. Can you tell your inspiration?
I'm never very good at answering this question because my inspiration for stories comes from so, so many different things, it's hard to unpick it all again when the story has been told.

With *Duckface* I remember wanting to stick up for kids who are always taking selfies, I think they get a reputation from older people as being vain when, I think a lot of the time, it's wanting to have some control over how you're presenting yourself to the world. Also even if you are just vain there's nothing wrong with that! If you know you're looking great why not take a pic, haha!

Boarding School is a very strange story and it changed so many times when I was writing it so I really have no idea! It started with the characters though, a curious, overlooked young girl and her good-natured, yet spoiled younger brother. I built the world around them.

Q4. Both of your stories focus on the power of friendship, especially between teenage girls. Why do you think this is so important?
I didn't have a very good time when I was in secondary school, I was badly bullied and my home life was quite tumultuous at times. My friendships with other girls (and my Mum, but that's another story) at that time were what got me through. I suppose my stories are often trying to say thanks to them.

Q5. Do you have a favourite retro Tammy & Jinty character?
I loved Fran from *Fran of the Floods*. She was so brave, practical, confident, and sensible. Quite the opposite of me as a young girl!

Q6. Each of your stories has superpowers in them. Do you have a favourite superhero?
I'm actually not very knowledgeable about superheroes. I enjoyed the Ryan North run on **Squirrel Girl** very much though, and Kate Leth's **Hellcat** series was a hoot. I like **Doctor Who** a lot too – does she count as a superhero? She has time-travel powers I guess, so why not!

Q7. Would you rather have lightning powers, the power to make everything you posted online come true, or the power to take perfect selfies every time?
Ooh, I wouldn't want to accidentally hurt anyone so not the lightning... and I post some bonkers stuff online sometimes so that sounds dangerous too! I am, however, absolutely dreadful at selfies so I'll take that one please!

SCRIPT RACHAEL SMITH • **ART** YISHAN LI • **LETTERS** JIM CAMPBELL

DEAR BLOG—

BEFORE MY USUAL WEEKLY POEM, I'D LIKE TO TELL YOU A LITTLE ABOUT MYSELF.

NOT THAT IT BOTHERS ME. I HAVE BETTER THINGS TO BE DOING THAN SHOPPING AND TAKING ENDLESS PICTURES OF MYSELF, WHICH IS ALL THE POPULAR KIDS DO.

MY NAME IS LOTTIE. I AM AN **EXCELLENT** POET AND WRITER AND — DUE TO THIS EXCELLENCE — I AM **VERY** UNPOPULAR AT SCHOOL. JEALOUSY IS AN UGLY THING, BLOG.

duckface.

NO, I WANT TO READ AND WRITE AND... **LEARN. MY** PICTURES ARE OF EXCITING PLACES I TRAVEL TO OR INTERESTING PARAGRAPHS I WISH TO SHARE WITH THE WORLD.

prettyviews #photojournal #exploretocreate

Liked by Mom

2 DAYS AGO

...BUT OF COURSE I DON'T CARE ABOUT THAT! I AM A **MUCH** BETTER PERSON THAN THOSE IN THE SELFIE-TAKING, VACUOUS, **POPULAR** CROWD. YOU'D NEVER CATCH **ME** DRAGGING OTHERS DOWN LIKE **THEY** DO.

MY PICTURES...RARELY GET ANY LIKES ON INSTAGRAM...

THAT HAVING BEEN SAID...

MIA IS BY FAR THE WORST.

MIA IS THE SUBJECT OF TODAY'S POEM.

COME ON, LOTTIE. DO THE RIGHT THING.

BEAUTIFUL MIA
I'M GLAD THAT YOU ARE HERE

YOU TAKE PRIDE IN YOUR APPEARANCE
AND MY UNWANTED INTERFERENCE

MUCH TO MY ALARM
HAS CAUSED YOU SO MUCH HARM

THERE'S NOTHING WRONG WITH BEING YOU
WE JUST HAVE DIFFERENT POINTS OF VIEW

I WISH YOUR LIPS WOULD GO BACK TO HOW THEY WERE
AS I HAD NO RIGHT TO BE YOUR SILENCER

≡SIGH≡

SHARE

MIA?

Oh, THANK GOD!

GLAD YOU'RE FEELING BETTER, MIA.

Oh! HI! CHARLOTTE, ISN'T IT?

Uh, LOTTIE's FINE...

HI, LOTTIE. SORRY, I WAS DISTRACTED TAKING SELFIES! I TAKE WAY TOO MANY...

WHY... DO YOU TAKE SO MANY SELFIES?

ARGH, IS IT ANNOYING? I'M A BIT SELF-CONSCIOUS. TAKING SELFIES JUST MAKES ME FEEL IN CONTROL OF HOW I LOOK.

SELF-CONSCIOUS?! BUT...YOU'RE PERFECT.

HAHA! YOU'RE VERY KIND BUT I'M NOT!

I'M NOT LIKE YOU-- I DON'T HAVE ANYTHING LIKE YOUR WRITING TALENT.

THE TEACHERS THINK YOU'RE A GENIUS!

I--WHAT? THEY DO NOT!

ANYWAY...YOU DO HAVE TALENT. YOUR PHOTOS ARE REALLY BEAUTIFUL.

WOW... THANK YOU, LOTTIE!

TWO WEEKS LATER...

the end.

Boarding School

SCRIPT RACHAEL SMITH • ART YISHAN LI • COLOURS PIPPA BOWLAND • LETTERS JIM CAMPBELL

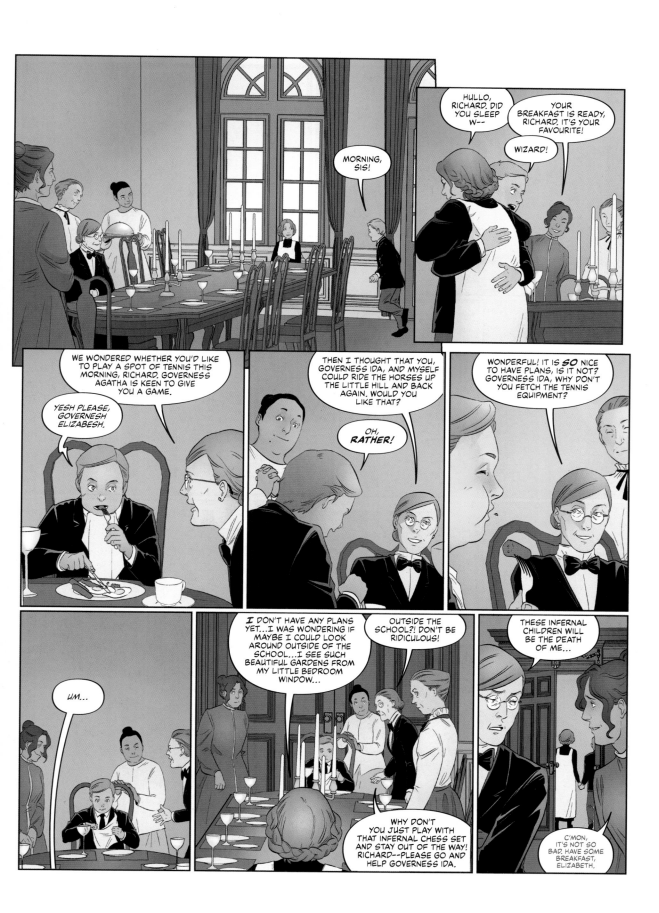

31

I'M VERY LUCKY REALLY...I HAVE THE RUN OF THIS WHOLE SCHOOL TO MYSELF EVERY DAY...

THERE CAN'T BE MANY CHILDREN THAT HAVE THAT...THERE'S REALLY NO NEED FOR ME TO FEEL THIS ROTTEN.

I JUST WISH I COULD HAVE SOME OF THE ATTENTION RICHARD GETS. HE IS AWFULLY CHARMING AND ATHLETIC THOUGH. PERHAPS I AM SIMPLY VERY DULL...

COME NOW, TABATHA. THAT'S NO WAY TO THINK. I'LL FIND A NICE SUNNY SPOT TO SIT IN AND PLAY CHESS AGAINST MYSELF. THAT WAY I'LL ALWAYS WIN...!

WHAT'S THIS?

I SAY! HOW BEAUTIFUL! SINCE THE GOVERNESSES WANT TO SPEND ALL THEIR TIME WITH RICHARD I'M SURE THEY WON'T NOTICE IF I PEEK OUTSIDE THE SCHOOL GROUNDS THIS ONE TIME...

OH!

OH!

OH! OH!

OO 'ECK!

32

--AND THEN GOVERNESH IDA PLAYED HIDE AND SHEEK WIV ME AND WE ATE THE RESHT OF THE RHUBARB AND CUSTARDS. SHE SAID I WAS THE *BESHT* AT HIDING.

THAT'S WONDERFUL, RICHARD. YOU ARE FEELING *CALM* AND *RELAXED* AFTER YOUR ACTIVITIES TODAY, I TRUST?

YESH, GOVERNESH ELIZABETH.

"I'D BE WELL ANNOYED IF THAT WERE ME. AREN'T YOU ANNOYED?"

DON'T YOU WANT TO KNOW HOW I SPENT *MY* DAY?

I IMAGINE YOU WASTED YOUR DAY PLAYING CHESS AND LOUNGING IN THE SUN... AM I RIGHT?

WELL... YES BUT--

THEN WHY ON *EARTH* ARE YOU INTERRUPTING OUR MEAL WITH OUTBURSTS LIKE THAT WHEN YOU HAVE NOTHING INTERESTING TO SAY... SILLY GIRL.

I MET SOMEONE WITH A MAGIC BOX ACTUALLY BUT MAYBE THAT'S JUST ME BEING SILLY, TOO...

YOU MET SOMEONE?! WHO?! WHERE WERE YOU?! ANSWER ME, GIRL!

WHAT'S A 'MAGIC BOX', SIS?

OH, RICHARD, IT WAS FASCINATING! THIS BOX CAN SEND MESSAGES AND MAKE PICTURES AND ALL SORTS!

ENOUGH!

I'LL NOT HAVE YOU FILLING RICHARD'S HEAD WITH NONSENSE! YOU'RE TO GO STRAIGHT TO BED RIGHT NOW! NO TALKING TO *ANYONE* TONIGHT!

BUT--

NOW!

KNOCK KNOCK

MHM... GOVERNESS... LUELLA?

NO, IT'S JUST ME, I NEED TO TALK TO YOU, RICHARD.

TABATHA! YOU CAN'T BE HERE! GOVERNESS ELIZABETH SAID--

SHH, IT'S ALL RIGHT...I NEED TO TALK TO YOU IN PRIVATE AND THIS IS THE ONLY TIME--

I DON'T WANT TO GET INTO TROUBLE!

RICHARD, LISTEN, I THINK THE GOVERNESSES ARE KEEPING THINGS FROM US...THINGS ABOUT THE WORLD OUTSIDE. I DON'T THINK IT'S LIKE HOW **WE** LIVE...

SHUT UP!

SHHH...RICHARD, I THINK WE SHOULD CONSIDER LEAVING THE SCHOOL... JUST TO SEE.

AREN'T YOU CURIOUS?

ARGH!

SHAAAA--!

35

THE NEXT MORNING...

WELL, IF I'M GOING TO CONTINUE TO BE IGNORED BY EVERYONE I MIGHT AS WELL TAKE ADVANTAGE OF IT!

HALF AN HOUR LATER...

WHAT SORT OF THING ARE WE LOOKIN' FOR, THEN?

ANYTHING THAT MIGHT TELL US MORE ABOUT MY BROTHER'S... *STRANGE POWERS.*

GOSH, STACY...IT WAS FRIGHTENING...

THIS IS THE GOVERNESSES' PRIVATE CHAMBERS...DOES YOUR MAGIC BOX OPEN LOCKED DOORS?

NO CHILDREN ALLOWED

IT'S A *PHONE*, TABBY, NOT A *SONIC SCREWDRIVER!*

MY BOOTS ADVANTAGE CARD MIGHT DO IT THOUGH...

MORE MYSTERIES!

THREE... TWO...

OO 'ECK...

C'MON THEN, NO POINT STANDIN' THERE GAWKIN'! LET'S INVESTIGATE!

TABBY...YOU NEED TO SEE THIS.

Log #1072

Weapon 'Tabatha':
Female has still not shown any signs of powers. Rehabilitation might still be possible.

Weapon 'Richard':
Incident last night.
Keeping subject entertained and calm for the time being.
Suspected too dangerous for rehabilitation.
Termination request sent.

'TERMINATION REQUEST'?

I DON'T UNDERSTAND...ARE WE MEANT TO BE *WEAPONS?*

I DON'T CARE IF WE DON'T UNDERSTAND IT ALL--WE NEED TO GET YOU OUT OF HERE *NOW!*

I CAN'T GO WITHOUT RICHARD.

WELL, YOU CAN'T STAY HERE EITHER! THINK ABOUT IT, TABBY--HOW ARE *YOU* EVEN GOING TO PROTECT HIM FROM ALL *THIS?!*

SOMEONE TAUGHT ME RECENTLY THAT IT'S DANGEROUS TO UNDERESTIMATE A YOUNG WOMAN LIKE THAT...

URGHHHH...*FINE!* LET'S COME UP WITH A PLAN THEN! CAN WE AT LEAST GET OUT OF THIS CREEPY LAB, THOUGH?!

DEAL!

I WAS STARTING TO WORRY!

RICHARD, THIS IS STACY.

HULLO...

I GOT THIS FOR YOU. THERE'S A LITTLE CAVE ABOUT TWO HOURS FROM HERE THAT YOU CAN SPEND THE NIGHT IN. THAT'S ALL I WAS ABLE TO FIGURE OUT, SOZ. HAD TO HELP MY DAD EARLIER WITH WORK.

THIS IS PERFECT, STACY, THANK YOU. BUT...WE WON'T NEED A MAP IF WE HAVE YOU AND YOUR MAGIC BOX...*UM, PHONE.* WILL WE?

TABBY, I...I NEVER SAID I'D BE ABLE TO COME WITH YOU...

OH! WELL, YES OF COURSE...HOW VERY STUPID OF ME TO ASSUME...I'M SORRY...

NO, NO, IT'S JUST I NEED TO LOOK AFTER MY DAD AND...I SHOULD REALLY STAY TO KEEP AN EYE ON THINGS HERE TOO. WHO KNOWS WHAT THOSE CREEPY GOVERNESSES ARE UP TO.

I'VE BEEN KEEPING SOME OF MY MATES IN THE LOOP WITH MY PHONE... MAGIC BOX. SO I'M NOT ON MY OWN.

YES, YES, OF COURSE. I'M SORRY...YOU'RE JUST THE FIRST FRIEND I'VE EVER HAD.

TABBY, I--

WAIT!

ARE WE LEAVING *TONIGHT?!*

YOU... DIDN'T **TELL** HIM?!

RICHARD... PLEASE STAY CALM...WE HAVE NO CHOICE, YOU HAVE TO TRUST ME...

NO! NO NO NO NO!

HEY, RICHARD... WANNA SEE THE NEW CLOTHES I GOT YOU?

I DON'T **NEED** NEW CLOTHES! I--

OH! WIZARD!

AND WHAT D'YOU RECKON TO MY OLD JEANS FOR YOUR SISTER?

GOVERNESS ELIZABETH SAYS GIRLS SHOULDN'T WEAR **TROUSERS.**

YEAH...IT'S REALLY GOOD THAT WE'RE GETTING YOU OUT OF THERE...

NOPE...

YOU'VE GOT FAR TOO INVOLVED IN ALL THIS. THIS CAN ONLY END BADLY FOR YOU.

C'MON, STACE. THAT'S A RUBBISH WAY TO THINK. THOSE TWO NEED ALL THE HELP THEY CAN GET. AND BESIDES, YOU'VE GOT ALL YOUR MATES ON THE END OF A MAGIC BOX! TIME TO INVESTIGATE.

NOPE...

BINGO!

THIS IS A BLESSING IN DISGUISE. THIS ABSURD *BABYSITTING* JOB WAS ALWAYS BENEATH US.

IT'S HARDLY BABYSITTING, ELIZABETH!

WE WERE PROTECTING THE WORLD FROM WEAPONS! EXPERIMENTS GONE WRONG!

THE GIRL WAS ALMOST READY FOR REHABILITATION!

WE MUST FIND THEM, KILL THEM, AND MOVE ON WITH OUR LIVES! THIS IS THE PERFECT EXCUSE.

snap

OH CRAP...

GET HER!

CRAP CRAP CRAP!

TABATHA...

...ARE WE MONSTERS?

NO, LITTLE BROTHER.

WE ARE LEGENDS.

THE END

Sally was a Cat

SALLY BIGGS WAS IN ONE OF HER MOODS.

IT'S ALL RIGHT FOR YOU, PATCHES. YOU DON'T KNOW WHAT IT'S LIKE TO HAVE PEOPLE BELLOWING AT YOU ALL DAY... DO THIS, DO THAT, DO THE OTHER! I'M JUST A SLAVE, THAT'S WHAT I AM!

WHAT A LIFE! SCHOOL... HOMEWORK... SCHOOL... HOMEWORK... THAT'S ALL I EVER GET! WHAT HAVE I DONE TO DESERVE IT?

TELL YOU WHAT! I'D SWAP PLACES WITH YOU ANY DAY OF THE WEEK!

YOU WOULD, EH? WELL, YOU JUST HAPPEN TO HAVE COME TO THE RIGHT PUSS, BECAUSE MY ANCESTORS COME FROM A LONG LINE OF WITCHES' CATS AND WE KNOW A THING OR TWO ABOUT MAGIC!

HOLD ON WHILE I WORK MYSELF UP A BIT. IT'S A TRICKY SPELL!

I MUST BE DREAMING!

OOO-ER! HE'S GOING ALL SORT OF FUNNY... GETTING BIGGER! AND... AND HIS FACE IS CHANGING!

AT SCHOOL...

HSSSS, PATCHES! IF YOU CHANGE ME BACK, I'LL GIVE YOU FISH EVERY MORNING, PROMISE!

EVEN SCHOOL DINNERS ARE BETTER THAN THAT. HOPPIT, I'VE GOT TO REPORT TO MISS FROST FOR MATHS!

HOPE MISS FROST COMES DOWN ON THE FELINE FRAUD LIKE A TON OF BRICKS. IN FACT, I'LL JOLLY WELL SEE THAT SHE DOES... THAT'LL SHOW PATCHES THAT BEING A SCHOOLGIRL ISN'T ALL HONEY!

AND DURING BREAK...

THIS IS THE BOOK. HEE, HEE, OLD FROSTY HATES SMUDGES, SHE'LL GO BERSERK WHEN SHE SEES THIS!

BUT...

YES, IT'S ALL MY FAULT, MISS FROST... IF I WASN'T SO KIND TO MY CAT, HE WOULDN'T FOLLOW ME TO SCHOOL AND TREAD ALL OVER MY SCHOOL BOOKS. THERE HE IS NOW... PINING FOR ME.

HOW VERY TOUCHING! FAR FROM BLAMING YOU, SALLY, YOU ARE TO BE COMMENDED FOR SHOWING SUCH KINDNESS TO DUMB ANIMALS.

GAH! WHAT FELINE CUNNING! I GIVE UP!

BUT THEN, THAT EVENING, JUST ONE WORD CHANGED EVERYTHING!

SALLEEEEEY!

ER...YES, MUM?

BATH!

NO! I CAN'T DO IT! I...I WON'T!

OF COURSE! CATS HATE WATER! COME TO THINK OF IT, YOU HAVEN'T HAD A BATH SINCE YOU BECAME ME! I DON'T BELIEVE YOU'VE EVEN WASHED YOUR NECK. MY NECK!

meet the creator

DANI

Q1. How did you start drawing comics?
I started drawing comics as a kid in order to change the endings in stories that I read and didn't like or wished to be different. Nothing special, just some panels of my own version of the story... Then I got into it and started participating in small comics contests in Greece and ended up doing my own self-published books after school.

Q2. What's your top advice for making a comic?
My advice for making a comic is to finish the whole thing. At some point we have all started working on this really special story but never moved past the character/world creation and the first pages. It's so important to always try to finish what you have started even if it's not perfect (it's never going to be), as it's the best way of learning your craft and getting better at it.

Q3. Which artists or comics influence your art?
Growing up I got exposed to many European comics through some Greek magazines and anthologies and then moved on to reading some American and Asian stuff. I now realize that one of my first influences in comics has been Sergio Toppi, then Mike Mignola and Eduardo Risso. But passing through art school gave me a lot of visual stimuli too – I get really inspired by Picasso, Pollock, Warhol and many more.

I think that if you are into arts the best thing you can do is to be open to all the forms rather than just staying in your lane. You can be a comics creator but still get influenced by sculptors, film or theatre directors, fashion designers, musicians etc. This is the way for the creativity to thrive.

Q4. Do you have a favourite retro Tammy & Jinty character?
Since I live in Greece unfortunately I didn't have access to **Tammy & Jinty** growing up and still haven't read any but am planning to whenever I find the chance, and recover the lost ground!

Q5. Your story 'The Enigma Variation' featured time travel and code breaking. What was your favourite thing to draw in this comic?
I really enjoyed drawing the Enigma time machine in this comic and the 1960s time period as I liked doing the research a lot. I think that in every comic what I end up enjoying the most is every new thing or place I get to draw, especially things I wouldn't think of drawing otherwise.

Q6. Have you ever used a secret code to communicate with your friends?
No, but I've developed certain expressions with the people who are the closest to me like my sister or my best friend. We might change the words a bit or have inside jokes and certain looks only we understand. So I guess in a way we do have a secret code!

Q7. If you could travel back to any time in history, which would it be?
It would be really interesting to visit ancient civilizations just to see how things were face to face and then even further back in time and see first hand everything that has been lost in time and we don't even know about!

THE NEXT DAY. THE ANNIVERSARY OF THE DAY TURING CRACKED ENIGMA.

YOU EACH HAVE YOUR TASKS AND ROLES. CODE SENDERS AND RECEIVERS, COMPILERS AND COURIERS, AND OF COURSE HUT 8 TEAM WITH THE BOMBE AND ENIGMA ITSELF.

ENJOY AND *LEARN!*

THIRTY MINUTES LATER, HUT 8.

I THINK SHE'S FINALLY LOST IT.

SHE NAMED HER OWN LAPTOP CHRISTOPHER, JESS. WE *KNOW* SHE'S CRAZY AND YOU AND I KEEP HER SANE. THOUGH NOW I KINDA WISH I'D BROUGHT POPCORN...

READY?

FOR WH--

--AT EXACTLY?

WHO THE BLAZES ARE YOU AND WHAT ARE YOU DOING IN HERE?!

THIS AREA IS ENTIRELY OFF LIMITS TO ALL STAFF EXCEPT MY TEAM!

CHRISTOPHER! YOU *LOST* HIM, PROFESSOR TURING!

HOW COULD YOU--*ANYONE*-- POSSIBLY KNOW--

LET ME TALK. YOU LISTEN. WE HAVE ALL THE TIME IN THE WORLD...

THREE HOURS LATER...

DO YOU HAVE ANY IDEA WHAT'S GOING ON?

SOMETHING ABOUT NOT BEING IN KANSAS ANY MORE?

...SO ALL YOU NEED ARE **SOME** OF THE SEQUENCE ITERATIONS WITHIN THE CODED MESSAGES AND CHRISTOPHER CAN FILL IN THE BLANKS.

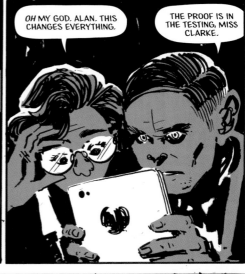

OH MY GOD. ALAN. THIS CHANGES EVERYTHING.

THE PROOF IS IN THE TESTING, MISS CLARKE.

IT WORKS. I CAN'T BELIEVE...

BUT IT WORKS!

CLICK! CLICK! CLICK!

YOU THINK HE'D SHOW A BIT MORE GRATITUDE.

WHAT'S THIS?

A GIFT FROM THE FUTURE. I'LL LEAVE IT TO YOU TO DECIDE HOW TO PUT THE CONTENTS TO USE, PROFESSOR.

SEE YA TOMORROW, DOC BROWN!

Rebecca

It was so lovely to meet you. Our mutual acquaintance lacks flair with people; hence he tasked me with writing these words.

Attached you will find the address of my family solicitor and a cipher that unlocks a deposit box. He wanted you to have it.

THE END

IN THE COLD DARK

SCRIPT MATT GIBBS • **ART** V.V. GLASS • **LETTERS** MIKE STOCK

IT'S SO HOT...

...I'M SWEATING BUCKETS!

MUK-OPPP!

WHAT HAVE YOU DONE?! YOU BASHED THEIR HEAD IN--

WHAT?! NO... I MEAN, IT'S NOT LIKE *WE* KILLED THEM!

WHAT DO YOU MEAN *WE*?

YOU SHOULD TELL LEELA...

TELL ME WHAT, AIMEE?

THEY LOOK IN PRETTY GOOD CONDITION, ALL THINGS CONSIDERED.

I'M SO, SO SORRY! IT WAS... I MEAN, IT JUST--

IT'S NOT HOLLY'S FAULT, I DISTRACTED HER.

HONESTLY, IT'S FINE! SKULL'S NORMALLY THE HIGHEST POINT, AS EVERYTHING ELSE COLLAPSES, AND IT CAN BE A HOLLOW CAVITY... HENCE THE POP WHEN YOU HIT IT.

ANYWAY, TRY TO GET THIS RECORDED AND LIFTED TODAY.

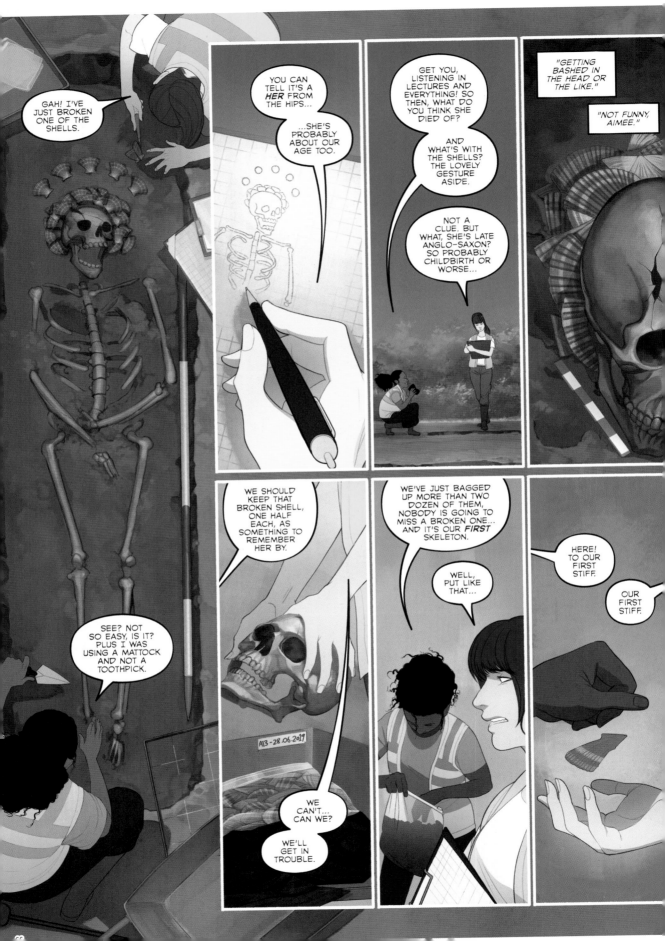

Holly
you fancy this
d? there be the
kings lynn to
oid! : DD
sure! but something quiet
don't want to Topsham Ten myself again...
anywho night hols!!
FWWOOOOSHHH
WOOOO
OOOSHH
!

I STILL DON'T UNDERSTAND HOW WE HAD THE SAME DREAM?

THESE *STUPID* KEYS... AH, GOT IT...

CLICK

BUT THE DREAM, THE DETAILS... IT WAS SO VIVID...

AND FOR IT TO BE *SO* SIMILAR?

JUST TRUST ME ON THIS... SHE WANTS THE SHELL BACK.

COME ON!

WOOOSSHHHA HFFWWO OSSHHHA

WHAT WAS THAT? I THOUGHT I...

DID YOU HEAR SOMEONE OUT THERE?

IT'S NOTHING... PROBABLY JUST THE WIND...

LET'S JUST GET THIS OVER WITH.

WWOOOSSHHH

ERR, DO YOU THINK WE SHOULD SAY SOMETHING? NOW WE'VE GIVEN THEM BACK...

WE'RE SORRY.

WE DIDN'T KNOW HOW SPECIAL THE SHELLS WERE... I MEAN, ARE TO YOU...

...BUT PLEASE, WE'VE PUT THEM BACK NOW, AND WE ARE SO VERY SORRY.

YEAH, WE'RE SO, SO SORRY...

"HOW DO WE KNOW IF IT WORKED?"

"THERE'S ONLY ONE WAY TO FIND OUT... SLEEP WELL, AIMS."

"YEAH, AND YOU. PLEASANT DREAMS..."

THE END

SCRIPT KATE ASHWIN • **ART** KEL McDONALD • **LETTERS** MIKE STOCK

MAISIE'S Magic Eye

COME ON, THIS WAY!

A-ARE YOU SURE, MAISIE?

YEAH, IF WE DON'T GO HOME THE USUAL WAY, MAYBE WE CAN AVOID--

ME?

OH DEAR, WHAT A PITY. THAT COAT ISN'T REGULATION. I'M GOING TO HAVE TO CONFISCATE IT.

NOT A CHANCE, NORA! YOU CAN'T JUST--

IT'S OKAY...

...WE DON'T WANT ANY TROUBLE WITH A PREFECT.

QUITE RIGHT.

SEE YOU TOMORROW, MOUSEY MEL...!

YOU SHOULD STAND UP FOR YOURSELF AGAINST BULLIES LIKE HER!

I... I KNOW, IT'S JUST...

"...I'M NOT AS BRAVE AS YOU."

WOAH!

FWSSH!

NO WAY!

KRR-ACK

WOW...

HUH. NOW THERE'S AN IDEA...!

YOU LOOK CHEERY THIS MORNING.

AND... TIRED? IS THAT A LEAF IN YOUR HAIR?

I WAS UP ALL NIGHT ON AN IMPORTANT MISSION.

MAKING YOU THE WORLD'S BEST BEST-FRIEND PRESENT!

OH WOW, MAISIE, IT'S... UH... UM--

DEFINITELY NOT REGULATION.

UGH, NOT AGAIN!

BETTER HAND IT OVER OR I'LL JUST HAVE TO REPORT YOU.

O-OKAY, NORA.

WHAT?! NO WAY!

NORA, WHY DON'T YOU JUST--

BACK OFF!

WUH?!

I... I'LL LET YOU OFF JUST THIS ONCE, MOUSEY!

SCRIPT & ART ANDY W. CLIFT • **LETTERS** MIKE STC

AFFIRMATIVE ACTION

It was all because of the stupid school trip. I was looking forward to it! It was my chance to talk to him, I knew it.

ANCIENT GREEK MYTH + MAGIC

HI, JUSTINE.

H-HI, TOM. UM, YOU LIKE THE EXHIBIT? THAT, UM, ATHENA IS GOOD, ISN'T IT?

I'm not great at talking to boys, but it was going pretty well.

OH!

HAHAHA!

SO, WHAT ARE YOU DOING AFTER SCHOOL? YOU...

...JUSTINE?

ARE YOU ALRIGHT?

OH...

Until I ran away.

LET ME HELP.

SHE TOUCHED IT! THAT SMELL IS NEVER COMING OFF.

WHAT'S WRONG WITH YOU?!

THANK YOU, JUSTINE. I HAVE SOMETHING FOR YOU.

OH NO, I COULDN'T! I DID WHAT ANYONE WOULD.

YET NO-ONE ELSE DID. THIS MIRROR WILL SHOW YOU AS YOU ARE.

NEEDING LIPPY?

OH, GOD, TOM!

I thought I'd fixed it. But it's like I was cursed or something.

JUSTINE! HEAR MY CALL!

HUH?

THERE'S A *GODDESS* IN MY MIRROR..!

YOU'RE A BIT FULL OF YOURSELF, AREN'T YOU? I'LL SEE YOU AROUND, JUSTINE.

SLAM

WIZARD BOY!

GOOD. YOU HAVE ANSWERED MY CALL.

YOU, JUSTINE, HAVE BEEN CHOSEN BY I, ATHENA!

WHAT?!

YOU SAW ONE IN NEED, AND RISKING YOUR OWN DESIRES, YOU AIDED ME.

I'VE CHOSEN NO HERO IN MILLENNIA. BUT THE WORLD NEEDS ONE NOW!

Only, it wasn't a curse. It was a job offer.

The uniform is cool, and the job was even cooler.

THAT WAS THE JAR OF PANDORA.

BOX, YOU MEAN? FULL OF, UM, SOMETHING BAD?

PANDORA CAPTURED THE *SPIRITS OF MONSTROUS CREATURES*, THINGS NOW DISMISSED AS MYTH, IN THAT JAR.

THEY CAN ESCAPE IT ONCE MORE. THEY WILL SEEK OUT SOULS TO POSEESS. THEY START WITH--

TOM? WHAT'S HAPPENING TO HIM?!

But then, the boy I like, he got in trouble.

TOM!

USE YOUR BOW, BEFORE HE CAN DO ANY DAMAGE!

NO! DOESN'T THIS THING AIM ITSELF?

WHAT DO I DO NOW? WHERE ARE YOU GOING?!

And the great thing was, my job meant I could help him!

THE BEST WAY TO TRAP A MINOTAUR IS IN A *LABYRINTH*. BUT SUCH THINGS ARE NOT OF YOUR TIME.

YOU MIGHT BE SURPRISED...

THE END

behind the scenes

THE CAT GIRL

The Cat Girl was a comic which ran in **Tammy** in 1971, although it originally began in a different girls' comic, **Sally** in 1969. *The Cat Girl* is Cathy Carter, the daughter of a detective, who discovers a magical catsuit which gives her all the powers of a cat!

In the 1970s, girls were often stereotyped as weaker as and less capable than boys – something that we know to be untrue - and in this comic Cathy's father constantly underestimates her because she is a girl. The joke is on him though, as Cathy is the one who always solves his crimes. We don't know who originally wrote this story, but it seems like they were writing for girls who felt like they weren't being taken seriously by their parents, just because they were a girl.

This short extract from the original *Cat Girl* is followed by *The Return of Cat Girl*, by RAMZEE and Elkys Nova. In this cracking comic we meet Claire, the daughter of the original Cat Girl, and are plunged into a colourful, fun adventure of crime, cats and explosions!

Girls of colour were not often the heroes of these older comics. Although there was some exceptions, for example, Nadine the Black heroine of **Jinty's** *Life's a Ball for Nadine*, the majority of heroines in girls' comics, like *The Cat Girl*, were white girls. Many people of colour live in the UK, but they were underrepresented in old comics. In RAMZEE's sequel, he makes the new Cat Girl a biracial heroine, increasing the heroic representation of the many girls of colour who live in the UK.

Agile as an acrobat, quick as a lightning flash... this is the astonishing story of ordinary Cathy who was to become known as

THE CAT GIRL

MY DAD'S A PRIVATE DETECTIVE. HE'S ALSO A VERY IMPATIENT MAN, AND AN ABSENT-MINDED ONE, TOO. HE WON'T ADMIT IT BUT HE IS, AND—WAIT, I CAN HEAR HIM CALLING! I THINK YOU'RE ABOUT TO GET A DEMONSTRATION

CATHY, WHERE'S MY TIE? HOW CAN I GO OUT ON A JOB WITHOUT A TIE?

YOU PUT IT ON BEFORE TEA TO SAVE MISLAYING IT—REMEMBER?

THAT'S MY GIRL, SHARP AS A NEEDLE. I'M OFF, THEN. WISH ME LUCK BECAUSE IF I PULL THIS JOB OFF WE CAN PAY THE RENT

GOOD LUCK, DAD— HERE, TAKE THIS SCARF, IT'S A COLD EVENING

I'D LOOKED AFTER DAD SINCE MUM DIED (THOUGH **HE** WOULD HAVE SAID HE LOOKED AFTER ME). I LIKED TO KEEP AN EYE ON HIM—THAT'S WHY I RUSHED UP TO THE ATTIC AS SOON AS HE'D GONE

I'LL GET THE OLD TELESCOPE. WITH THAT I SHOULD BE ABLE TO SEE THE BUILDING DAD'S KEEPING GUARD ON TONIGHT

IT WAS AN INSURANCE BLOCK ON WHICH DAD HAD SUSPECTED THERE WAS TO BE AN ATTEMPTED BREAK-IN

THERE'S THE TELESCOPE— OOOCH! BLOW THAT CASKET!

THE CASKET HAD BEEN SENT TO DAD FROM AN ECCENTRIC BUT GRATEFUL OLD FRIEND. HE HADN'T BEEN ABLE TO GET IT OPEN SO HE'D PUT IT IN THE LOFT OUT OF THE WAY. BUT NOW THE LID FLEW UP

WONDER WHAT'S INSIDE—HALLO, LOOKS LIKE SOME SORT OF COSTUME

I SPRANG DOWN THE FIRE ESCAPE STEPS IN GREAT BOUNDS—WHOLE FLIGHTS AT A TIME

WHAT'S THE MATTER WITH ME? I'M SUDDENLY AS AGILE AS A CAT. A *CAT!* THAT'S IT! IT'S THIS SUIT!

NOTHING SEEMED IMPOSSIBLE WHILE I WORE THAT SUIT, BUT NOTHING

RECKON THAT WITCH DOCTOR KNEW A THING OR TWO —HIS CAT SUIT'S TURNED ME INTO A FELINE!

AHA, THERE'S THE INSURANCE BLOCK—THIS IS WHERE I GET OFF

I LEAPED, ROLLED OVER SIX TIMES AND SPRANG—CATLIKE—TO MY FEET

THEN I WAS SHINNING UP A DRAINPIPE AS EASY AS GOING UPSTAIRS

DAD MUST HAVE PUT UP A PRETTY GOOD FIGHT BECAUSE HE WAS ONLY JUST GOING DOWN AS I ARRIVED ON THE SCENE

WELL, THIS SHOULDN'T BE ANY PROBLEM TO A PUSS LIKE ME. I RECKON THERE'S A FEW SURPRISES IN STORE FOR THOSE THUGS—*HEY, YOU TWO!*

DON'T MISS SEEING CATHY THE CAT IN ACTION NEXT MONDAY. SHE'S TERRIFIC!

The CAT GIRL

I WASN'T ORDINARY CATHY ANY MORE. I WAS A CAT GIRL, WITH SPRINGS IN MY HEELS

YOU LEAVE MY DAD ALONE!

YEE—OW!

YOU'RE HIS DAUGHTER? YOU LOOK MORE LIKE A BLOOMING CAT GIRL TO ME!

MY PRIVATE DETECTIVE DAD HAD BEEN TRYING TO STOP A BREAK-IN OVER AT AN INSURANCE BLOCK. THE THIEVES HAD KNOCKED HIM OUT COLD. BUT NOW MY WONDERFUL CAT SUIT GAVE ME SUPER CAT-LIKE POWERS..

THAT'S RIGHT! CAT GIRL CATHY!

OUCH!

SO THIS IS WHAT YOU BROKE INTO THE BLOCK FOR? A CONFIDENTIAL FILE!

SHE'S GOT THE PAPERS!

STOP HER!

THIS IS WHERE I GIVE THEM ANOTHER SURPRISE

WITH ONE GIGANTIC LEAP I REACHED THE OPPOSITE ROOF—THANKS TO THE CAT SUIT

YOU SHOULDN'T TAKE THINGS THAT DON'T BELONG TO YOU!

WHAT IS SHE? A GIRL OR A CAT? GIVES ME THE CREEPS!

ME, TOO. LET'S CLEAR OFF AND TELL THE EAGLE WHAT'S HAPPENED. HE'LL KNOW WHAT TO DO

IT WAS AMAZING! EVEN MY HEARING WAS AS FINELY-ATTUNED AS A PUSSY'S. I'D HEARD EVERY WORD

SO THE EAGLE'S THE MASTER MIND BEHIND THIS BREAK-IN—DAD'S ARCH ENEMY. NO WONDER DAD WANTED TO FOIL HIM. AND THAT REMINDS ME— I'D BETTER GIVE DAD'S CONFIDENCE A BOOST.

NOW THE COAST WAS CLEAR I DOUBLED BACK ON MY TRACKS TO DAD. HE WAS JUST COMING ROUND WHEN I CREPT UP AND PLACED THE FILE BEHIND HIM

MY POOR HEAD!

HIS FACE A MINUTE LATER WAS ENOUGH TO MAKE ME PURR WITH PLEASURE

THIS IS THE FILE I SAW THEM STEAL—AND NOW THEY'VE DROPPED IT! I MUST HAVE GIVEN THEM A SCARE ALL RIGHT!

I RACED HOME. BY THE TIME DAD GOT BACK, I WAS JUST ORDINARY CATHY AGAIN...MY CAT SUIT SAFELY TUCKED AWAY IN THE KITCHEN DRAWER

I PUT UP QUITE A FIGHT, AS YOU CAN IMAGINE, CATHY—AND IT WORKED. SCARED THOSE THUGS OFF GOOD AND PROPER

CAREFUL, DAD. THAT'S THE SUGAR BOWL YOU'RE STIRRING!

LATER, HE SHOWED ME THE CONTENTS OF THE CONFIDENTIAL FILE

WHY SHOULD THEY WANT TO STEAL THIS? CHARTS—DIAGRAMS. CAN'T MAKE HEAD NOR TAIL OF IT

LOOK AT IT IN THE MORNING WHEN YOU'RE FEELING FRESHER. THE ANSWER MIGHT COME TO YOU THEN

THOSE DIAGRAMS WERE A BIT BAFFLING. THEY SEEMED TO BE SCALE DRAWINGS OF A PLACE CALLED HARRISON'S HALL, WITH LOTS OF ARROWS AND RED DOTTED LINES ACROSS THEM

SUDDENLY, THE LIGHTS WENT OUT

IT'S ONLY A FUSE, CATHY—LEAVE IT TO ME

WONDER IF I CAN SEE IN THE DARK LIKE A CAT? I'LL PUT MY SUIT ON AND TRY

IT WORKED!

GOSH, I GET MORE LIKE A CAT EVERY TIME I WEAR THIS SUIT. NOW TO MEND THE FUSE WHILE DAD'S FUMBLING ABOUT!

WHAT A SHOCK!

ON
OFF

IT'S NOT A FUSE AT ALL. SOMEONE'S DELIBERATELY TURNED OUR LIGHTS OFF AT THE MAIN SWITCH!

meet the creator
RAMZEE

Q1. How did you start making comics?
I started making comics after going to my first small press indie comics fair back in — *yikes* — 2011? I was so blown away by the different types of comics being made and inspired by the passion and the humour of the creators.

Q2. What's your advice for making a comic?
Start small. My first comic was a book of three 5-page stories where I learned how to tell a story in a small amount of pages and short stories are quicker to produce so you get the satisfaction of finishing something sooner.

Q3. Your story in this collection, *Cat Girl Returns*, is based on an older story, *The Cat Girl*. What interested you about telling the story of Claire and her magical cat suit?
The old *Cat Girl* stories had a really cool mix of superhero and detective stories. Cathy had this magical cat suit that gave her all these cool extraordinary abilities which she'd use to help her detective Dad solve mysteries. It was like *Spider-Man* meets *Inspector Gadget*.

CONCRETE SURFER, ART BY CHRISTINE ELLINGHAM

WHAT ARE WE WAITING FOR? CAROL, ARE YOU JOINING US?

ER . . . NO, THANKS.

Q4. How did you reimagine the old *Cat Girl* comic for a new audience?
I've always wanted to write a zany story about how a superhero would deal with the modern world of social media and this was my chance to scratch that itch with *Cat Girl*. I also thought it would be interesting if Cathy, the original Cat Girl, grew up to become a detective herself and her daughter Claire took up the mantle of Cat Girl by accident. I wanted Claire to also be biracial because you don't get many characters who look like her in UK comics.

Q5. If you have the catsuit, you can harness all the abilities of a cat. If you could have one cat super-power, what would it be?
Easy — nine lives! I would go exploring around the world and take all sorts of crazy fun risks. Ride a barrel down Niagara Falls? Sure, I have eight more lives to spare! Turn life into a video game lol!

Q6. What comics are you reading right now?
Right now I'm reading **Superman's Pal Jimmy Olsen** by Matt Fraction & Steve Lieber, **Dragon Hoops** by Gene Luen Yang and **The Oracle Code** by Marieke Nijkamp.

Q7. Do you have a favourite classic *Tammy & Jinty* (or other girls' comic) character?
Besides Cat Girl, I think Jean Everidge aka *The Concrete Surfer* is super rad. I love *School for Eggheads* and *Maisie's Magic Eye* is pretty cool.

MAYBE MUM WILL HAVE SOMETHING.

THIS IS THE CLOSET OF MY DREAMS!

WHAT'S THIS?

OOH! COOL AND VINTAGE!

JUST IN TIME!

TAXI

"LUCKY THAT THIS SAFE ROOM DOOR IS THICKER THAN A CASINO VAULT..."

...OR WE WOULD'VE BEEN BBQ COPS.

IN JUST ONE NIGHT, YOU'VE HAD A PAINTING STOLEN, WHICH YOU DID NOT REPORT, AND THEN SOMEONE TURNED YOUR HOME INTO A BONFIRE WITH YOU STILL IN IT.

WHAT ARE YOU MIXED UP IN, MR FALCONER?

I AM AN ANTIQUES DEALER, DETECTIVE. I WAS APPROACHED BY SOMEONE OFFERING A LOST PICASSO FOR NEXT TO NOTHING IF I SOLD HIS TREASURES OFF TO MY CLIENTELE.

THEY'RE NOT TREASURES, THEY'RE STOLEN PROPERTY.

WHAT ARE THE CHANCES THAT AFTER TAKING THEIR MONEY, THIS SOMEONE RELIEVED YOUR CLIENTS OF THEIR "TREASURES" TOO.

AND YOU, BEING THE ONLY LINK BACK TO HIM, HAD TO BE WIPED OUT.

WHAT HAVE YOU FOUND, ANNIE?

WE FOUND FALCONER'S CLIENT LIST ON HIS CLOUD AND CROSS REFERENCED IT WITH OUR INCIDENT REPORTS.

AND?

THEY'VE ALL BEEN RECENT VICTIMS OF BREAK-INS EXCEPT ONE...

"...LOTTIE ROSE."

EVER HEARD OF *"LIVING IN THE MOMENT"*?

HORS D'OEURVES?

SO WEIRD! THE SMELL IS SO INTENSE I CAN LITERALLY TASTE THEM!

EW! NO THANKS!

AAAGH!

A HIGH, FRIGHTENING SCREAM!

WHY IS EVERYONE STILL DANCING?

GOT A PASS, KID?

SOMEBODY'S IN TROUBLE BACK THERE, SIR! DIDN'T YOU HEAR?

NO PASS, NO ENTRY. PUSH OFF!

AS YOU WISH.

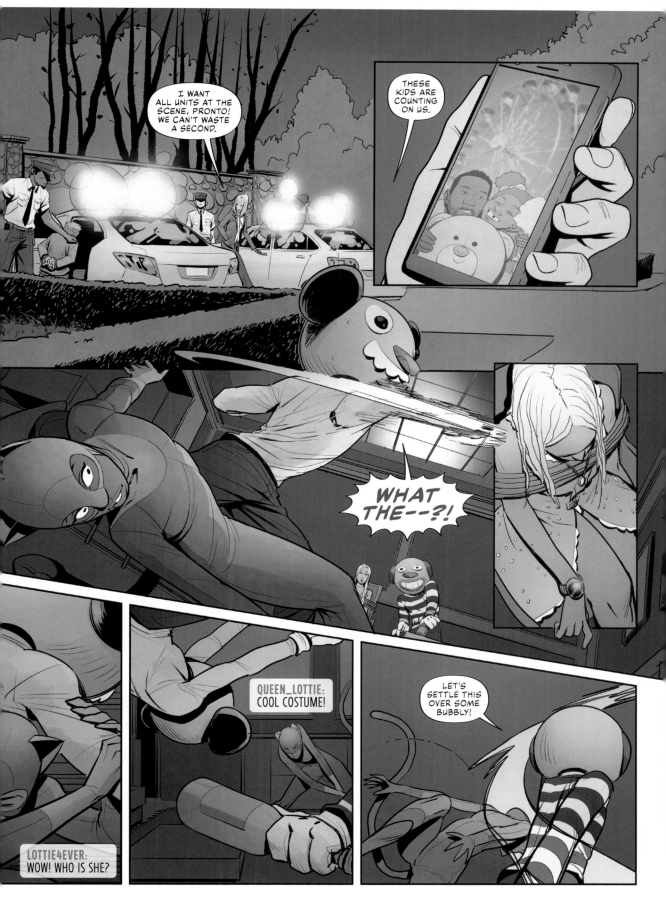

DUDE, I'M NOT OLD ENOUGH TO BUY AN ENERGY DRINK.

THANKS! WHO ARE YOU?

CALL ME, UH, CAT GIRL.

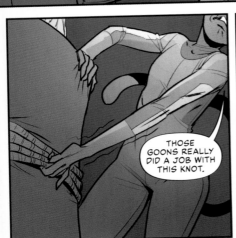

THOSE GOONS REALLY DID A JOB WITH THIS KNOT.

WOW! THESE CLAWS ARE SHARPER THAN I THOUGHT.

Maddy96: OMG! OUR LOTTIE IS TOAST!

danny: 😨😨😨

THE DIAMONDS. *NOW!*

TAKE A SEAT!

TO THE BACK OF THE HOTEL, LADS.

HERE I AM, RUNNING FOR MY LIFE WITH A MYSTERIOUS CAT GIRL.

WHAT ARE YOU DOING?

KEEPING MY FOLLOWERS IN THE LOOP.

BLAM

AND THEM, TOO!

MISSED US?

MAXXINE: NO FAIR! CAT GIRL SUX!

ARRGH!

CAT GIRL!

LUCKY FOR ME, I EARNT MY KARATE BADGE AT GUIDES.

UNLUCKY FOR THEM, THERE'S EIGHT PAINFUL FLIGHTS OF STAIRS BELOW THEM.

FREEZE!

STAND DOWN! IT'S LOTTIE ROSE.

IS THE NECKLACE SAFE?

YES, OFFICER. BUT I'M FEELING EPIC FOBO THOU.

FOBO?

FEAR OF BEING OFFLINE.

BUT YOU'VE ONLY BEEN OFF FOR A MINUTE?

AND?

WE'LL NEED YOUR NECKLACE FOR SAFEKEEPING.

SURE, OFFICER.

OMG! NOT THIS AGAIN!

A FOUL SMELL SETS MY TEETH ON EDGE AND A SHIVER OF FEAR THROUGH MY BODY.

sniff
sniff

A HOARD OF STOLEN ART AND JEWELLERY, AMONG THEM A £200 MILLION DIAMOND NECKLACE, WERE RECOVERED AND RETURNED TO THEIR RIGHTFUL OWNERS TODAY.

MANY OF THE ITEMS WERE FOUND IN THE UNWITTING HANDS OF PEOPLE LIKE YOUTUBE CELEBRITY LOTTIE ROSE

A FAN SENT IT TO ME. I DIDN'T KNOW IT WAS STOLEN! SO FOLLOWERS, DON'T STEAL, PLEASE SUBSCRIBE AND BUY MY MERCH, OK? **NAMASTE!**

NewsTV

BREAKING NEWS: STOLEN LOOT FOUND

BUT THE MASTERMIND BEHIND IT ALL-- **THE EAGLE,** REMAINS AT LARGE.

I'M REALLY PROUD OF WHAT YOU DID TONIGHT, PUDDING, BUT NO MORE.

THERE ARE CRIMINALS A LOT MORE DANGEROUS THAN THOSE YOU MET TONIGHT. ONES WHO'LL STOP AT NOTHING TO GET WHAT THEY WANT.

I DON'T WANT **ANOTHER** KNOCK ON MY DOOR, CLAIRE, BECAUSE IF YOU DIE, I DIE TOO.

DON'T WORRY, MUM.

THERE'S ONLY ROOM FOR ONE CRIME FIGHTER IN OUR FAMILY.

SORRY I BORROWED YOUR COSTUME WITHOUT ASKING.

SO YOU SHOULD BE.

NOW PUT IT BACK. I'VE GOT A REPORT TO WRITE.

OH, HON-- WHEN YOU WORE IT...

...YOU DIDN'T EXPERIENCE ANYTHING, UH, ODD? DID YOU?

NO. SHOULD I HAVE?

NO. IT'S JUST THAT IT USED TO GET A LITTLE, UH, ITCHY BACK IN THE DAY.

RIGHT? 'NIGHT, MUM.

THE END

HI THERE! I'M OLIVIA! I'M AN EDITOR!

AND I'M GEMMA! I'M A DESIGNER!

AND TOGETHER WE'RE THE EDITORIAL TEAM ON *TAMMY & JINTY REMIXED!*

Behind the Scenes

Meet the Team! ♥

ART BY PETITECREME

OUR JOB WAS TO COLLECT UP THE STORIES WHICH MAKE UP THIS BOOK!

THIS BOOK CONTAINS A MIX OF OLD AND NEW STORIES, AND IT WAS OUR JOB TO DECIDE THE BEST WAY TO PRESENT THEM TO YOU, THE READER.

MY JOB IS TO DECIDE ON THE BOOK'S CONTENT. LUCKILY, WE ALREADY HAD A BUNCH OF GREAT STORIES!

I ALSO HAD TO GO THROUGH OUR ARCHIVES AND CHOOSE OLDER STORIES WHICH I WANTED TO REPRINT, AND THEN DECIDE WHAT ORDER THE STORIES SHOULD GO IN.

I ALSO HAD TO INTERVIEW THE AUTHORS AND GATHER ALL THE NECESSARY INFORMATION THAT GEMMA NEEDED TO PUT TOGETHER THIS BOOK!

MY JOB IS TO MAKE EVERYTHING FIT TOGETHER AND LOOK GREAT! BEING A DESIGNER MEANS MAKING ALL THE COMIC PAGES AND THE LETTERING LOOK GOOD.

IT'S ALSO MY JOB TO DESIGN EVERYTHING FROM THE COVER TO THE CONTENTS PAGE. I WANT TO MAKE SURE THE READER PICKS THIS UP AND ENJOYS EVERYTHING ON THESE PAGES.

Tammy & Jinty Special 2019: Cover by **Lisa Henke**

Tammy & Jinty Special 2019: Pin up by **Kit Buss**

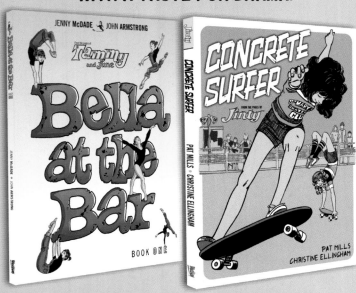

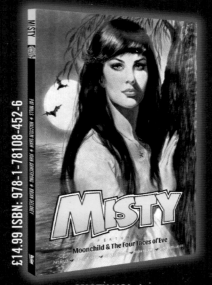
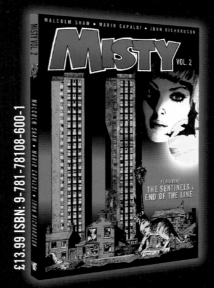